THIS WALKER BOOK BELONGS TO:

For Mum

First published 2004 by Walker Books Ltd
87 Vauxhall Walk, London SE11 5HJ

This edition published 2010

2 4 6 8 10 9 7 5 3 1

This book has been typeset in Aunt Mildred

Printed in Singapore

British Library Cataloguing in Publication Data:
a catalogue record for this book is available from the British Library

ISBN 978-1-4063-2501-0

www.walker.co.uk

HOORAY, IT'S MY BIRTHDAY!

Hi, Tyler!

Tor Freeman

WALKER BOOKS

AND SUBSIDIARIES

LONDON • BOSTON • SYDNEY • AUCKLAND

When Dinah
had her birthday,
Tyler planned a wonderful
surprise for her.
In the afternoon,
while they were painting
a picture together,
there was a knock at the door.
"I'll get it," said Tyler.

TOOT TOOT TOOT TOOT

Brown Rabbit
burst into the room
playing a brass horn.
And what was
the tune?
Happy Birthday
to You!

Next Lemur came in with some flowers.

"Happy birthday, Dinah," she said.

"Thank you for my flowers," said Dinah.

Then Croccy
popped in
and gave Dinah
an enormous
crocodile
hug.

SQUEEZE

"Hello, Croccy," said Dinah.

"It's my birthday."

"Happy birthday,"

said Croccy.

And Croccy gave them all

one of her famous crocodile rides.

The last to arrive, in a rush,
was Otter, with Dan and Jed Frog.
"Hop!" and "Pop!"
said Dan and Jed.
"Happy birthday, Dinah!"
said Otter.

Hop!

Pop!

He gave her
the red balloon.

For party games
they played skipping
and ring-a-ring
o' roses.

And they danced rock 'n' roll
while Otter blew the horn.

Then Tyler said, "It's time for tea.
But first, Dinah, shut your eyes."
This was going to be the best bit,
Dinah's wonderful surprise.

1 ...

2 ...

3 ...

Wow!
What
an enormous
cake!

"Surprise!"

shouted everyone,
suddenly jumping out
from behind the cake.

"HAPPY BIRTHDAY
TO YOU!"

Also by Tor Freeman

ISBN 978-1-4063-0516-6

Praise for *Sleepy Places*

"A gentle, lilting picture book to share as you
cosy up before bedtime." *Junior*

Available from all good bookstores

www.walker.co.uk